THE DEEP-SEA ADVENTURE SERIES

JAMES C. COLEMAN
Professor of Psychology
University of California
at Los Angeles

FRANCES BERRES
Assistant Director, Clinic School
University of California
at Los Angeles

FRANK M. HEWETT
Assistant Professor of Education
University of California
at Los Angeles

WILLIAM S. BRISCOE
Professor of Education Emeritus
University of California
at Los Angeles

Andy   Salty   Submarine Captain   Tom

Illustrations by JOSEPH MANISCALCO

Frogmen
in Action

Carlos   Dan   Bill

HARR WAGNER PUBLISHING COMPANY • San Francisco

TABLE OF CONTENTS

Chapter One

THE STRANGE SUBMARINE

Dan turned his face away from the cold wind that came over the deck of the *Sea Watch*. Far off in the distance he could see snow-covered mountains. The *Sea Watch* was sailing north to a Navy base. Dan looked toward the shore for a minute. Then he went inside the boat.

"That wind goes right through you, Bill," said Dan to the man at the wheel.

"These waters in the north are very cold," said Bill.

"We will have to watch for ice on the deck," said Dan. "It is not easy to walk out there any more."

"Where is Carlos?" asked Bill.

"He is looking over our diving gear," answered Dan. "We have to be ready to go to work as soon as we reach the Navy base."

"I will be just as glad to stay on deck while you and Carlos go down into that cold water," said Bill.

"So will I," said Andy, as he walked in. "Just

looking at all that ice and snow is enough for me."

A parrot sat on Andy's shoulder. It was Salty. Salty was another member of the crew of the *Sea Watch*.

"We brought heavy diving suits with us to keep out the cold of the water," said Dan.

"Just the same," said Andy, "I'm glad I am the cook and not a diver on this boat."

"I'm the cook," said Salty. "I'm the cook."

"I think Salty is glad to be staying on deck, too," laughed Dan.

"He is," said Andy. "It has been so cold the last few days that Salty has not talked very much."

"It will take more than the cold to stop Salty from talking," laughed Bill.

"When are we going to get to the Navy base, Bill?" asked Andy.

"It won't be long now," said Bill.

Dan and the crew of the *Sea Watch* were on their way to a Navy base in the north. The Navy needed divers to salvage several ships which had sunk in these waters.

Dan and Carlos were divers. Dan was the skipper of the *Sea Watch*. Carlos was his first mate. Bill ran the boat for Dan, and Andy cooked for the crew.

"Skipper," called Carlos from the deck. "Come outside, fast!"

Dan ran out on deck. Andy ran outside after him. Carlos stood pointing out to sea.

2

"Look," he said, "out there!"

Dan and Andy looked to where Carlos was pointing. Some distance away they saw a long, dark submarine just coming to the surface of the water. They could not tell which country it was from.

The men could see a big gun on the deck. Then they saw the top hatch of the submarine open. Several crew members came out on the deck. One of them pointed toward the *Sea Watch*.

"I don't like the looks of this," said Dan. "Several ships have been sunk in these waters."

"You mean sunk by a submarine?" cried Andy.

"No one is sure," said Dan slowly. "No crew member of any of the ships was ever found."

Andy ran inside the *Sea Watch*. He came back with a life jacket in his hand.

"Look at Andy," said Carlos. "He is afraid that . . ."

But Dan stopped him. "Get to the radio fast, Carlos," he said. "Send a message to the Navy base. Tell them a submarine has just surfaced near us. Tell them that we cannot make out what country it is from."

Carlos ran inside the boat to send the radio message. Dan and Andy stayed on deck watching the submarine.

Several more crew members came out of the hatch on the deck of the submarine. They stood talking together and pointing to the *Sea Watch*.

"What are they going to do?" asked Andy.

3

"I don't know," said Dan. "But I hope they dive and get out of here."

"What do you think, skipper?" called Bill from inside the *Sea Watch*.

"Keep the boat moving at full speed ahead, Bill," Dan called back. "All we can do is wait and see."

Carlos came back on deck.

"I got the message off to the Navy base," he said. "They are sending a plane to help us. There is one near here on a mission."

"I hope we won't need the plane's help," said Dan. "But it is good to know that one is coming."

The strange submarine moved through the water near the *Sea Watch*.

"Andy," said Dan, "you had better get life jackets for all of us. We may be in for real trouble."

Andy went inside the boat and brought out life jackets for Dan and Carlos. Then he took one inside to Bill.

"We cannot last long in this cold water with only life jackets on," said Carlos.

"I know," said Dan. "I hope we won't need them. I don't like to think of swimming in water this cold."

Andy came back on deck. There was a troubled look on his face.

"Why don't they dive and get out of here?" he said.

But as the men watched the submarine, they saw

4

that it was not going to dive. The submarine crew ran to the gun on the deck and pointed it at the *Sea Watch*.

"Take cover down on the deck, men!" cried Dan.

Bill stayed at the wheel while the other men dropped down on the deck. The boat was going at full speed, but the submarine was getting closer.

Then the men heard an explosion! The submarine had fired on them! The shell crashed down across the bow and into the water. The explosion sent a great wave of water down on the deck of the *Sea Watch*.

"Try to keep away from those shells," called Dan to Bill. "Turn the *Sea Watch* one way, then another."

The next shell crashed into the water on the starboard side of the ship. The boat rocked from the explosion. Bill ran the boat at full speed. He turned it first one way, then another as it went through the water.

"If only the Navy plane would get here," said Carlos. "That might save us."

"That's right," said Dan. "The sub would dive if a plane came over."

Another shell was fired. Part of the topside of the *Sea Watch* was hit.

"A few more like that and we are through," said Andy.

The men waited for the next shell.

"Wait!" cried Dan. "What is that sound?"

The men looked up. They saw a Navy plane coming toward them.

"The Navy's here!" cried Carlos. "Never did a plane look so good to me before."

The men on the submarine saw the Navy plane, too. They left their gun and ran to the hatch. In no time at all, the submarine was diving. Soon it could not be seen on the surface.

The men of the *Sea Watch* stood up on the deck and waved to the plane as it flew over them.

"I hope it stays around until we get to the Navy base," said Andy. "That sub may come back."

"I think the plane will be watching us from now on," said Dan. "Radio the Navy base, Carlos, and tell them we are all right. Thank them for sending the plane, too."

Dan and Andy walked down the deck to see where the shell had hit the boat. They saw that it had destroyed a small part of the topside of the *Sea Watch*. But there was no real danger to the boat.

The *Sea Watch* sailed on up north. Several times a Navy plane flew over them.

Dan, Carlos, and Andy stood in the bow of the boat looking for the submarine.

As Dan looked out over the water, he saw something strange in the distance. He pointed it out to Carlos and Andy.

"Is that a fish?" asked Andy.

"It doesn't look like a fish to me," said Carlos.

Dan told Bill to take the *Sea Watch* over to the strange thing in the water.

As the boat pulled closer, the crew saw that it was a man swimming very slowly through the water.

"What's he got on?" asked Andy.

"It's a black rubber suit," said Carlos. "He looks like a U.D.T. frogman."

"U.D.T. What's that?" asked Andy.

"Underwater Demolition Team," answered Carlos. "The Navy frogmen are members of that team. They are trained up north here at the Navy base."

"The rubber suit makes him look like a fish from a distance," said Andy.

"The Navy frogmen swim like fish," said Carlos. "They are sent out to get secret information and to destroy underwater mines."

The *Sea Watch* sailed close to the frogman. When he saw the boat, the frogman started to swim slowly toward it.

Carlos and Andy pulled the frogman aboard. They took him inside the boat. At first the frogman did not have enough strength to talk. The crew of the *Sea Watch* helped him all they could. They all wanted to know one thing. Why was one Navy frogman swimming alone so far from shore?

9

Chapter Two

CARLOS TURNS FROGMAN

Slowly the frogman looked up at the men.

"All gone," he whispered over and over. "All gone."

"Take it easy," said Dan.

"All gone," said the frogman again.

"He will soon feel better in here away from the cold wind," said Andy.

In a while the frogman sat up and looked at the men around him. A look of worry was on his face.

"Who are you?" he asked.

"This is the *Sea Watch*," said Dan. "We are on our way to the Navy base to do salvage work."

The look of worry left the frogman's face.

"That's good," he said slowly.

"We picked you up in the water out there," said Dan.

"I didn't think I would be rescued," said the frogman. "I swam for a long time. I didn't think I would make it."

"You are all right now," said Dan.

The frogman looked at each one of the men.

"My name is Tom," he said, holding out his hand to Dan. "It is good to be on your boat. You saved my life."

"Glad to know you, Tom," said Dan.

Each crew member told the frogman his name. One by one the men held out their hands to him.

"What did you mean by, 'all gone'?" asked Carlos. "You said that over and over when we picked you up."

The look of worry came back on Tom's face.

"Did you see any more frogmen out there when you picked me up?" he asked.

"No, we didn't," answered Carlos.

"I was afraid of that," said Tom. "Then all of my team were killed."

"Who killed them?" asked Dan.

"This morning we were sent out on a mission," said Tom. "We were looking for a mine field which might have been placed in these waters to destroy our ships."

"I know several ships have sunk up here," said Dan. "But I had not heard about a mine field before."

"Even we were not sure about it," said Tom.

"Did you find the mine field?" asked Dan.

"Yes," said Tom. "After diving for some time, we found it. Our mission was to find out how many mines there were, how deep they were, and what they looked like. But we never had a chance to do it."

"Why not?" asked Carlos.

Tom went on. "A strange sub surfaced and began firing on us. I saw many of my team members killed by the sub's gun. I dived as deep as I could and escaped."

"That sounds like the same sub that shot at us," said Dan. He told Tom about the *Sea Watch* being fired at by the strange submarine.

"The sub must have stayed around these waters," said Tom. "I don't know what to make of it. Where could the sub have come from?"

"There must have been more trouble up here than we have heard about," said Dan.

"There has been much trouble," said Tom. "But the Navy is not going to let it go on. The U.D.T. frogmen will be back, and next time we will be ready for that sub."

Tom told Dan that, from what he had seen, there were mines in the water all around the *Sea Watch* now.

"All around us?" cried Andy. "Even if that sub didn't get us, the mines will!"

Carlos sent a message to the Navy base telling them that the *Sea Watch* had picked up the frogman. He told the Navy about the mines, too. A message came back asking the crew of the *Sea Watch* to get all the information it could about the mines.

12

"If I had any strength left," said Tom, "I would dive down and get more information about the mines. I would like to find out how close they are together and just how far they are under the surface of the water."

"Would that help the Navy to clear out the mines faster?" asked Carlos.

"I'm sure it would," answered Tom. "But I am afraid I cannot do it."

"But I can," said Carlos. He turned to Dan. "How about it, skipper? Why don't I dive down and look for the mines?"

"The water is too cold for skin diving," said Dan.

Carlos pointed to the frogman's heavy, black rubber suit. "I'll put on Tom's suit," he said. "He is about as big as I am. It should work out all right."

Dan thought for a minute. At last he said, "It is up to you, Carlos."

"I want to do it," said Carlos. "Will you let me use your gear, Tom?"

"Yes," said Tom, "if you are sure you want to try this."

"I would like to help the Navy," said Carlos. "And I have always wanted to try out a frogman's gear. Now is my chance."

The men helped Tom take off his rubber suit. Then they helped Carlos into it.

The rubber suit fit tightly around Carlos. Part of the suit fit over his feet. Rubber gloves covered his hands. Another part was like a helmet. It fit tightly around his head. Only Carlos' face was not covered by the black rubber suit. The suit was made to keep out the cold of the water.

Tom tied a small plastic pad on the rubber suit. This was to put information on. There was a pointed stick with it. When a frogman wants to put down information while he is underwater, he uses the stick to put the message on the plastic pad.

Then Carlos put the rubber flippers on over his feet. These would help him save his strength while swimming. They would help him swim fast, too. Carlos took the glass face mask from Tom. Through the glass in the mask, Carlos would be able to see very well underwater.

"I see how the frogmen get their name," said Andy. "With that gear on you look just like a frog, Carlos."

"Like a frog!" said Salty, the parrot. "Like a frog!"

"You will see how well that suit keeps out the cold of the water, too," said Tom. "Even a frog cannot swim as well as we can in water this cold."

"Even so, Carlos, don't stay in the water too long," said Dan. "You are not used to this cold water, yet."

"Don't worry," said Carlos.

16

Carlos walked over to the side of the *Sea Watch.*
He put on the glass face mask. At last he was ready.
Then he waved to the men and dived into the sea.

The men watched him dive down under the water.
Now and then, Carlos would have to come up for air.
He was a good skin diver and could hold his breath
for a long time underwater. He had been down almost
two minutes when he swam up to the surface for air.

"I see a mine down there," he called to the men on
the boat. "I am going down to get a better look."

Then Carlos was gone again under the water.

"We are going to have trouble getting the *Sea
Watch* out of here," said Dan to Tom, as they watched
for Carlos. "Just one mine could destroy this boat."

"I know," said Tom. "But Carlos may get enough
information so we can keep away from the mines."

Carlos swam down to the mine he had seen floating
under the surface. Its dark shape was not far away.

Mines are used to destroy ships. Each mine is
anchored in the water under the surface. When a
ship hits a mine, there is a big explosion. Many times
the ship is sunk. There is great danger to all ships in
mined waters because the crew of the ship cannot see
the mines. They never know when one is close by.

Carlos swam very close to the mine. Several times

he put information on the plastic pad with the pointed stick. Carlos wanted to take back all the information the Navy needed.

Carlos swam a distance and saw another mine. He looked to see how much distance there was between the two mines. Then Carlos had to swim to the surface for more air. By now he was some distance away from the *Sea Watch*. He waved to the men on the deck.

Carlos made another dive and swam on. He looked over each mine he came across. By now he had all the information he needed on the plastic pad.

As Carlos started to swim to the surface, he saw something strange ahead. It was a long, dark shape floating under the surface of the water. At first Carlos could not tell what it was. But as he swam closer, Carlos saw it was a submarine. It looked like the submarine that had attacked the *Sea Watch*!

As Carlos swam along looking at the submarine, something reached out and grabbed him! Before he could turn around, Carlos found he was held tightly. Carlos used all his strength and tried to pull away. But it was no use. Carlos was pulled slowly back through the water toward the submarine!

Chapter Three

THE U.D.T. FIGHTS BACK

Tom and the crew of the *Sea Watch* stood looking out at the water where they had last seen Carlos.

"Carlos is staying down a long time," said Tom.

"He has been down over two minutes, already," said Bill. "I don't like the looks of this, Dan."

The men turned and looked to starboard for Carlos. But they did not see him.

Three minutes went by. Dan began to worry. "Carlos must be in trouble down there!"

Dan ran to the other side of the boat. He took off his jacket and started to get ready to dive. Bill ran after him.

"Take the boat over to where we saw Carlos last, Bill," said Dan. "I am going down to find him."

Bill put his hand on Dan's shoulder. Dan turned and looked at him.

"It's no use, Dan," said Bill. "You won't have a chance in that cold water."

"I have to try to save Carlos," said Dan. "Get the boat over there fast, Bill!"

"Right away, skipper," said Bill.

He ran inside the boat and started up the motor. Bill took the boat over to where they had last seen Carlos.

Andy and Tom stood talking on the deck.

"I don't know if Dan should try this," said Tom. "One man lost is enough. There is not another rubber suit for him to put on. Dan cannot last long in this cold water."

Dan walked over to the men. "I should never have let Carlos go," said Dan. "But he wanted to do it very much. I have to try to save him."

"Carlos is a good man," said Andy slowly. "I hope you can find him."

Just then Dan called out to Bill to stop the boat. "This is close enough," he called. "I am going to dive down here and take a look."

Dan stood up on the side of the boat and dived into the water. He did not have on a rubber suit, and the cold of the water hit him fast.

Dan swam down under the water. He saw a mine in the water not far away. He swam around it, looking for Carlos. But Carlos was not to be seen. Dan swam on. But he could not find Carlos. At last Dan knew he had to have more air.

22

Once he was on the surface, Dan had trouble breathing. His strength was about gone from the cold. Dan did not want to give up. He wanted to find Carlos. But he saw it was no use. Slowly Dan swam back to the *Sea Watch*. The men pulled him aboard.

"It's no use," said Dan. "Carlos is gone."

Dan put his head in his hands. He had wanted very much to find Carlos.

"Carlos always tried to do everything well," said Andy. "This time he just could not do it."

"His strength must have given out," said Dan.

For a while, the men of the *Sea Watch* did not talk. They sat and thought about Carlos. It was not easy to think that they would never see him again.

After a while, they started for the Navy base. Dan told Bill what he knew about the mines.

Slowly Bill took the boat through the mine field.

All the men had on their life jackets. They knew that at any minute the boat might hit a mine.

After going very slowly for a long time, the *Sea Watch* reached open water and sailed at full speed for the Navy base.

The day was almost over when the *Sea Watch* reached the harbor at the Navy base. Some Navy men were waiting at the dock.

Tom went on shore first. He was taken to see Commander Martin of the U.D.T. Commander Martin wanted information about the frogmen team.

Soon Dan was called to see Commander Martin, too. The commander held out his hand when Dan walked in.

"It is good to know you, Dan," he said. "We are glad you made it here all right."

"Thank you, sir," said Dan. He sat down across from Commander Martin.

"I have heard about your first mate, Carlos," said the commander. "I heard he was trying to get information for us. He must have been a good man."

"Carlos was the best," said Dan.

The U.D.T. commander then asked Dan for information about the submarine. Dan told him all that he could.

"It sounds like the same submarine we have heard about before," said the commander.

"Do you think the mines were put in the sea by that sub?" said Dan.

"I am sure of it now," came the answer.

"What country is this submarine from?" asked Dan.

"That is the thing we don't know," answered the commander. "Several countries think it is one of our submarines. We have thought all along it was a submarine from another country. But ships from other

24

countries have been sunk as well as our ships. There is danger of war starting because of this!"

The commander stood up. As he walked around he said, "It is easy for trouble to start between countries this way. Each country thinks another country is sending out the sub. Before any of us knows the real answer, war could start."

"I never saw a sub like it before," said Dan.

"You are one of the few who has ever seen the sub and is still around to talk about it," said Commander Martin. "Several of our planes have seen it, but it has always dived before they could get a good look at it. All of the men on the ships that were sunk seem to have been killed. The sub must have killed any of the men who escaped the explosions of the mines."

"The sub didn't wait for us to get into the mine field," said Dan. "It fired on us first."

"It did that because you were not armed," said the commander. "It does not attack armed ships on the surface. It lets the mines take care of them."

"What are you going to do now?" asked Dan.

"First," said Commander Martin, "we are going to destroy the mine field. And this time our Underwater Demolition Teams will be ready for that sub."

The commander told Dan that the U.D.T. had more frogmen ready to go out again. This time they were going to be sent out from a Navy ship. The U.D.T.

frogmen would be covered from the air by Navy planes.

"The teams will be ready to take off from the ship in the morning," said the commander.

"From what I have heard, you won't need me for salvage work right away," said Dan. "Is there any chance of going along?"

"I don't see why not," said the commander. "Be on the dock soon after it gets dark."

"Thank you, sir," said Dan. "I'll be there."

Dan left the commander. He went back to the *Sea Watch* where Bill and Andy were waiting for him. Dan told them about his talk with the commander.

"It sounds like there is more trouble ahead," said Bill. "I am glad we are here to help."

"More trouble," said Salty, the parrot. "More trouble."

Dan told the men he would be gone for a day. He told Bill and Andy to work on the topside of the deck that had been hit.

Soon after dark, Dan went down to the Navy dock. The U.D.T. frogmen were going aboard a ship. Commander Martin took Dan aboard with him. In a few minutes the ship pulled out of the harbor. Dan looked out over the dark sea. He thought about Carlos as the Navy ship sailed on to the mine field.

Chapter Four

CLEARING THE MINE FIELD

The U.D.T. commander walked over to Dan.

"We will drop anchor soon," he said. "Then we will wait for morning before sending out our teams."

Dan saw several rubber boats on the deck.

"So those are the boats the frogmen use?" he said.

"Yes," was the answer. "Five frogmen can fit in one of those rubber boats, along with enough explosives for their mission."

"There must be great danger in a mine field with a boat full of explosives," said Dan.

"There is always danger in any of the work that the U.D.T. does," said the commander. "But these men know all about explosives and their use. Frogmen are trained to be ready for everything."

"I have heard that you give the men real training for this work," said Dan.

"We do!" said the commander. "Very few of those who want to be frogmen make it through training.

They have to be the best to last through our training."

"A man must have to swim very well before you will take him," said Dan.

"No, Dan," said the commander. "Many of our best men could not swim at all when they started. But if a man has what it takes, we train him right from the start. Soon he is in top shape."

The ship's motor stopped. Dan heard the anchor drop into the water. He knew they must be near the mine field.

"I'll see you in a while," said the commander. "I have to get the teams ready."

Dan saw Commander Martin call all of the frogmen together. They sat on the deck while the commander held up a map for them to see. A light was held on the map so the men could see it in the dark.

"Here is where we are," said the commander, pointing to the map. "And here is the mine field."

The map showed the mines, the distance between them, and how far under the surface they were floating.

"We are going to use two teams on this mission," the commander went on. "The rubber boats are ready. All the explosives you will need are waiting to be put aboard once the boats are in the water."

Commander Martin then went over the mission point by point.

"It is very important that you watch the time on

the mission," he said. "Any man not clear of the mine field when the explosives go off may be killed."

The frogmen watched the commander very closely. Each man knew his life might be lost if he did not do just what Commander Martin said.

"Now, is any man not clear about this mission?" the commander asked.

Not one of the frogmen said a thing.

"Good!" said the commander. "Let's get started."

The frogmen started to get ready at once. Each of them put on a heavy rubber suit. Soon they all stood by the side of the ship holding their glass face masks and rubber flippers in their hands.

Several of the men held small radios. These were covered tightly so that water could not hurt them. The men would send messages to each other as they worked. They would send messages back to the Navy ship, too.

As it started to get light, two rubber boats were let down into the water. One by one the frogmen dropped over the sides of the command ship into the small boats. Five men sat in each boat.

At the U.D.T. commander's signal, the small boats moved away very fast through the water.

Several Navy planes flew above, keeping a watch for the strange submarine.

Each boat headed for a part of the mine field. Each

team was to get more information on the mines. With the small radios, the teams would talk over the information with each other and with the command ship. After this, the work of clearing the mine field would start.

Soon the teams had all the information they needed.

Each frogman of Team 485 took some of the explosives from the bottom of the rubber boat. The explosives were ready to be tied on to the mines. Face masks and flippers were put on, and down into the water went the frogmen.

The frogmen swam down to where they knew the mines were. As they swam up to each mine, they used great care. They did not want to hit the mine. Even a small hit might fire the mine.

With great care the explosives were put in place. They were set to go off at a given time. The frogmen had to move fast.

Once they were through, all the team members got back into their rubber boat and moved away.

Then Team 485 called the commander over the radio by a code signal.

"U.D.T. Team 485 to command ship. Explosives are in place. Over."

"This is the command ship, 485. Are you clear of the mine field?" asked the commander.

"Yes, sir. We are standing by," was the answer.

"Good," said the commander. "Mines will go off as planned. Out."

The frogmen teams waited in their small boats.

All at once the mines were fired. Water shot far up into the air as the explosions took place.

As soon as the explosions were over, the men of Team 486 went into action in their part of the field.

The work of clearing the mine field went on all day. At last the teams had set off all the mines.

When the teams were back aboard the command ship, the commander called the frogmen together.

"Good work, men," he told them. "The mines are gone, and no one was hurt."

"What is our next move, sir?" asked one of the men.

"The plan will be told to all of you very soon," said the commander. "Now we have to get back."

The Navy ship pulled up anchor and headed for the base. Just before dark, they docked in the harbor. Dan thanked the commander for letting him go along.

"Glad to have you," said the commander.

"I'll be ready to start diving for salvage in the morning," said Dan.

"We may need your help in some other work," said the commander. "I have been thinking about a plan to destroy that sub for good."

31

Chapter Five

THE SECRET SUBMARINE BASE

When the *Sea Watch* left the mine field the day before, the crew thought that Carlos had lost his life in the cold water. But Carlos had not been killed.

Carlos was pulled slowly back through the water toward the submarine. He pulled with all his strength, but he could not get away.

Carlos was held by two men in black rubber suits. They had tanks of air on their backs. Rubber tubes came out of the tanks and went into the face masks to give them all the air they needed. These divers did not have to go to the surface of the water to get air.

Carlos needed air. He did not have a tank to give him air under the water.

All at once Carlos blacked out. When he came to, he was inside the submarine that had fired on the *Sea Watch*. Two men were standing over him.

"How much does your Navy know about the mines?" one of the men said to Carlos. He was heavy-set and had on glasses.

Carlos could not answer right away. It was not easy for him to talk. At last he said, "Where am I? What is this all about?"

"Answer the captain," said the other man. "How much does your Navy know about the mines?"

"I don't know," said Carlos slowly.

"What do you mean?" the man cried. "Tell us what we want to know, or you will get hurt."

"I am not a U.D.T. frogman," said Carlos.

"But you have on a U.D.T. suit," said the captain.

Carlos told the men he was a crew member of the boat they had shot at that morning. He told them how he got the frogman suit from Tom.

"How can we be sure you are not a U.D.T. frogman?" asked the captain's mate.

"There is no way you can be sure," said Carlos. "But I tell you I am not a frogman. I am a deep-sea diver. I was to do salvage work for the Navy."

"A deep-sea diver!" said the captain. "Then you can still be of use to us. Our deep-sea diver has been hurt, and he cannot work for a time."

"Why did you fire at us?" asked Carlos.

"You ask too much," said the captain's mate.

"Let him ask all he wants to," said the captain.

"He will never escape. I think he knows he will have to go along with us or be killed."

Then the captain turned back to Carlos.

"So you want to know why we are out to destroy ships, do you?" the captain went on. "Well, I will tell you. We are going to start a war!"

"How can one submarine start a war?" asked Carlos.

"Listen," said the captain. "Each time we destroy a ship, the country that ship is from thinks some other country has sunk it. This starts trouble between countries. As more ships are sunk, there is more trouble. Soon there will be war."

Carlos listened closely to the captain's plan.

"I have men and guns waiting in many countries," the captain went on. "Once war starts, my men will attack. They will take over the countries one at a time, and soon I will be in command!"

"Such a plan will never work," said Carlos.

"No?" said the captain. "Wait until you see my secret base and the guns and explosives I have there."

Carlos had never heard of such a plan. He wanted to know more. There might be a way he could stop these men. But right now he knew he must wait. Until a chance came, he would have to go along with these men.

"You do not talk," laughed the captain. "You are afraid for your country. Well, you should be afraid.

But you will be all right if you do what we tell you to do."

"I see," said Carlos. "I will dive for you."

"Good," said the captain. "Now we had better head back to the base. The Navy plane may be back."

As the men walked away, the captain called back to Carlos, "You will be closely watched. My men have been told to kill you if you start any trouble."

Carlos was left alone. He thought about all that the captain had said. Then he closed his eyes. Before long Carlos went to sleep.

Carlos did not know how long he had been sleeping when he heard two crew members talking near him. Carlos did not open his eyes. The men thought he was still sleeping. Carlos heard everything they said.

"The captain said we would surface off Shadow Mountain," said one of the men. "But we won't go into the base through the big underwater tunnel."

"Why not?" asked the other man.

"Some rocks dropped down and covered the opening," was the answer. "We must use explosives to clear the big tunnel so the sub can go into the base."

"What about the small tunnel just under the surface?" asked the other man. "Is that open?"

"Yes," answered the first man. "Some men will

swim into the base through the small tunnel." Then he laughed, "No one would ever think a secret submarine base was inside Shadow Mountain!"

"What are the next plans?" asked the other man.

"The captain plans to destroy the Navy base," answered the first man. "Then war will start for sure."

The two men walked away, and Carlos opened his eyes. So, they planned to destroy the Navy base! Carlos knew he must do something at once.

Just then the captain and mate walked in.

"My men tell me that you have been sleeping," said the captain. "That is good. You should be ready to go to work for us right away."

"What do you want me to do?" asked Carlos.

"I want you to go down and clear the opening of an underwater tunnel," said the captain. "We have all the deep-sea diving gear you will need. You will take explosives down to clear out some rocks."

"If you start any trouble," said the mate, "I will be waiting with this." He pulled out a knife and waved it before Carlos' eyes.

"We will surface in a few minutes," said the captain. "See that you are ready to go to work."

The two men left Carlos and walked away.

Carlos knew he would have to think fast. Then he saw the small plastic pad and pointed stick that were still tied to him. Carlos took off his rubber suit and other gear, but he held the plastic pad and pointed stick covered in his hand.

Soon a crew member came for him. He took Carlos up on deck. Carlos saw that the submarine was floating near a great mountain covered with ice and snow.

"That must be Shadow Mountain," he thought.

Carlos saw several men in rubber suits dive into the water. Carlos knew they must be going down to the small tunnel he had heard the men talking about.

One of the submarine crew members helped Carlos put on a diving suit. While no one was looking, Carlos put the plastic pad and stick into one of the heavy gloves he was going to put on. Soon he was ready to have the diving helmet put down over his head.

The mate showed him the explosives on the deck.

"Put these under the rocks," he said. "After you get back, we will fire the explosives from up here."

"All right," said Carlos. "Let's get this over with."

A small buoy had been anchored in the water over the opening of the tunnel. When Carlos saw the buoy, a plan began to take shape.

The diving helmet was put over Carlos' head. Then he was helped over the side of the submarine. Down he went into the cold water.

Once he was on the bottom, Carlos saw the buoy rope by the tunnel. He saw the rocks that had come

down over the opening of the tunnel. Carlos placed the explosives under the rocks. Then he signaled to be pulled up by pulling four times on the rope.

A diver is pulled up very slowly. As Carlos was being pulled up, he took the plastic pad and stick out of his glove. He had enough time to put a message on the pad.

Carlos was being pulled up next to the buoy rope. He was glad they had given him a knife in his diving gear. Carlos took it out and cut almost all the way through the buoy rope. Now only a small part of the rope held the buoy. When he was almost to the surface, Carlos tied the plastic pad to the bottom of the buoy.

Soon Carlos was back on the deck of the submarine. The captain's men had not seen him put the pad on the buoy. Carlos knew that if they had seen him they would have killed him.

After the explosives were fired, Carlos was sent down again. He found that the opening of the tunnel was clear. Now the submarine could go into the base.

It was almost dark when Carlos was pulled back up to the surface. While the men took off his diving suit, he looked out at the small buoy. All at once it started to float away. The rope had given way at just the right time. Slowly at first, then faster, the buoy floated away from the submarine!

Chapter Six

THE SEA WATCH'S MISSION

Back at the Navy base, Dan was called to see Commander Martin.

"I have talked with my men," said Commander Martin. "We have a plan we think may work."

Dan sat back and listened to the commander.

"We want to send the *Sea Watch* north of here where the sub was last seen," the commander started. "There may be a secret base up there. Your boat has been seen and shot at by the sub once already. If the sub sees you again, they will surface and attack you— thinking you are on a Navy mission."

"Which we would be," said Dan.

"That's right," said the commander. "But this time you will be ready for them. We will put a secret gun on the *Sea Watch*. The gun is small, but one well-placed shot could destroy the sub. We will send a demolition team with you, too. They will stand by to fire the gun and get information on the secret base."

"Do you think the sub will attack us knowing we might radio for help again?" asked Dan.

"I think they will attack you at once this time," answered the commander. "They waited too long to start firing the last time, and they know it."

The commander turned his eyes toward Dan.

"It is a big mission," he said. "What do you think?"

"We will be ready to go as soon as you want us to," said Dan. "My men want very much to help the Navy destroy that submarine."

"I knew what your answer would be, Dan," said Commander Martin. "My men are already getting everything you will need to put aboard the *Sea Watch*. I will be down to talk to you and your men soon."

"Very good, sir," said Dan. "We will be waiting."

Dan left the commander and went back to the *Sea Watch*. He told Bill and Andy about the mission.

"We will be ready," said Bill. "It sounds like there is real action ahead for us."

"Real action," said Salty. "Real action."

"You said it," said Dan. "How do you feel, Andy?"

"I'm ready," said Andy. "Just let me be sure my life jacket is aboard when we start off."

The men laughed at Andy.

Before long, Navy men brought the secret gun aboard the *Sea Watch*. It was put in place on the deck. The Navy men put a sonar set aboard, too.

The next morning five U.D.T. men came aboard with Commander Martin. One of the team members was Tom.

"I asked to come along on this mission," said Tom. "I want to be on hand when you see that sub again."

The men went over the plan with great care.

"All messages will be sent in code," said the commander. "The frogmen know the code and will work the radio. They will keep off the deck so that they will not be seen. That way the plan will not be given away."

Soon everything was ready. The crew and the U.D.T. men stood on the deck and waved to the commander on the dock. Then the *Sea Watch* pulled out of the harbor.

As the *Sea Watch* sailed north, Dan and Andy stood close to Bill at the wheel.

"Keep your eyes open, men," said Dan. "If we come across the sub, we want to be sure we are ready."

"I hope they try to start something," said Andy. "We will take care of them with that gun."

"That doesn't sound like the same Andy we used to know," laughed Bill.

"We all feel the way Andy does," said Dan, as he put his hand on Andy's shoulder. "Andy is an important part of this mission. He has to cook for a big crew now. And frogmen are always hungry."

"Always hungry," said Salty. "Always hungry."

"That's right," called Tom. "We are all waiting to try Andy's cooking."

Tom stood by one of the team members who sat listening to the sonar set. The sonar set would tell him when the *Sea Watch* came close to something.

"Have you heard anything yet?" asked Dan.

"Not yet," answered Tom. "There doesn't . . ."

Just then the man at the sonar set looked up.

"Something is coming over now," he whispered.

A sonar set sends out signals under the water. When something like a mine or a submarine is hit by one of the signals, the signal is shot back to the sonar set and makes a sound. The frogman at the sonar set had just heard the sound start. He knew something was out in the water.

"What does it sound like?" asked Tom.

"I don't know," came the answer. "This is strange. When I send the signals out far to the right or left, no sound comes back. It must be something small."

Dan told Bill to watch the water ahead.

After a while, Bill called out, "I think I see something some distance ahead, skipper. It might be what the sonar set is picking up."

Dan and Andy went out on the deck. They saw something small floating in the distance.

"Should I take the boat over to it?" called Bill.

Dan thought for a minute. Then he went back to where Tom and the other frogmen stood by the sonar set. Commander Martin had put Tom over the other frogmen. Dan and Tom were to work together while the *Sea Watch* was on this mission for the Navy.

"What do you think, Tom?" asked Dan.

"We are not picking up anything more in the water," said Tom, as he looked at the sonar set. "I don't think there is a mine field ahead."

"Then let's take a chance," said Dan. "Slow down our speed, Bill, and we will have a look."

The *Sea Watch* moved slowly toward the strange thing floating in the water. As the boat moved closer, Dan and Andy went out on deck to see it.

"That's a small buoy," said Dan. "It must have floated away from its anchoring. It's strange to see something like that up here. There are no other Navy bases around."

"What about the secret sub base?" said Andy.

"I was just thinking about that," said Dan. "Let's pull the buoy aboard and have a look at it. It may give us some important information."

Dan had Bill stop the boat. Andy and Dan pulled the buoy up on deck. They took it inside.

"What's that thing tied to the bottom?" asked Andy.

Tom grabbed a plastic pad that was tied to the buoy.

"Look!" he cried. "It's one of the U.D.T. pads."

Tom took the plastic pad off the buoy. He looked at it very closely. He saw that a message was on the pad.

"Listen to this," he cried. "There is a message on it. It's from Carlos!"

The men of the *Sea Watch* moved close to Tom and looked down at the pad. The message said:

SECRET SUB BASE INSIDE SHADOW MOUNTAIN. SHIPS SUNK TO START WAR BY MEN WHO WANT TO TAKE OVER ALL COUNTRIES. ATTACK ON NAVY BASE PLANNED.   CARLOS

"Carlos must be all right!" cried Andy.

"When Carlos didn't come up from the mine field, he must have been taken aboard the sub," said Bill.

"Then Carlos is being held at the secret sub base," said Dan. "This information tells us just what we want to know."

"I have heard of Shadow Mountain," said Tom. "It is a very big mountain covered with ice and snow. It comes right down to the shore."

"How could the sub base be inside such a mountain?" asked Bill.

"There may be an underwater tunnel among the rocks at the bottom of the mountain," said Tom.

48

Dan brought out a map for the men to look at.

"There it is," said Tom, pointing to a name on the map. "Shadow Mountain."

Dan looked at the map for a minute. Then he said, "It will take us about a day to reach there, Tom."

"Before we start out, we must clear with the Navy base and think out a plan," said Tom.

"Will you be able to rescue Carlos?" asked Andy.

"I hope so, Andy," said Tom. "Carlos was trying to help the Navy when he was lost. We will not let him down if there is any way we can save him."

One of the frogmen sent a code message to the Navy base. It told what had been found on the buoy.

Very soon an answer came back. It said:

ANCHOR IN COVE 962. SEND TEAM TO GET IN-
FORMATION ON BASE. IF SUBMARINE IS IN-
SIDE MOUNTAIN, DO NOT LET IT ESCAPE. NAVY
WILL HAVE PLANES, MEN READY. WILL WAIT
FOR YOUR MESSAGE BEFORE ATTACKING.

The men looked at the map again.

"Here is Cove 962," said Dan. "It is down along the shore not far from Shadow Mountain."

"We can take a rubber boat up the shore after dark," said Tom. "That way we will not be seen."

"Head for the cove, Bill," said Dan.

All day the *Sea Watch* headed north. When it got dark, the boat anchored.

The frogmen went right to sleep. They needed to be in top shape for the next day.

The crew of the *Sea Watch* sat and talked for a while.

"I cannot get over that message from Carlos," said Andy. "I never thought we would see him again."

"I hope he is all right," said Dan. "There is great danger from the men he is with."

"Think of their plan!" said Bill. "Trying to start a war so they can take over all countries. I hope they can be stopped."

"Let's turn in now," said Dan. "There is a big day ahead for all of us."

The men went to sleep. Before morning, they were up again. The day was almost over when Bill saw the cove off the starboard bow. He called out to Dan, "The cove is up ahead, skipper."

"Take the *Sea Watch* in," called back Dan.

Dan and Tom were on the starboard side of the boat. Far up the shore they could see a great mountain that stood out above all the others.

"There is Shadow Mountain," said Tom, pointing it out to Dan. "That is where the U.D.T. will be soon."

"What if you find trouble up there?" asked Dan. "Should we come after you?"

"No," answered Tom. "We will plan to be back

50

aboard the *Sea Watch* at a given time. If we are not back by that time, send a message to the Navy base. My men will have a code message ready to be sent. It will say that as far as you know we are lost."

"I hope we won't have to send that message," said Dan.

"We hope so, too," said Tom.

Once the *Sea Watch* was in the cove, the anchor was dropped. The U.D.T. frogmen began to get ready. Air was put in the rubber boat, and all the gear they needed was put into it. It was just getting dark as Tom called the frogmen together and went over the plan.

"We will take the rubber boat on shore here," he said, pointing to the map. "When there is enough light to see by, we will go to work. Four of us will swim out and dive among the rocks, looking for an opening of a tunnel. The other man will cover the rocks at the base of the mountain. He will look for an opening above the surface of the water."

The frogmen talked over the mission many times. At last it was time to go. The frogmen put on their rubber suits. They all had air tanks on their backs. Rubber tubes went from the tanks into the glass face masks.

One by one the frogmen got aboard the small boat.

"We will be seeing you," called Dan to the frogmen.
"I hope so," called back Tom.

Out through the dark went the small boat.

Soon the frogmen reached the shore. They pulled the boat up on the rocks and waited for morning.

As the first morning light came down on the sea, the frogmen started to work. One of the frogmen started looking among the rocks above the water. The other four frogmen swam out some distance from shore. In teams of two, they dived down and looked among the rocks under the water for a tunnel.

Tom and his teammate were the first to find the small tunnel just under the surface of the water. They came up and talked about a plan.

"We will swim through the tunnel and get a look at the inside of the base if we can," said Tom.

Then he told the other men to wait on the surface.

Tom and his teammate saw that the air in their tanks was coming through the rubber tubes all right. Then they dived down.

They swam through the opening of the tunnel. It was very dark inside. It was so dark that at first Tom and his teammate did not see two divers from the submarine swimming through the tunnel toward them!

54

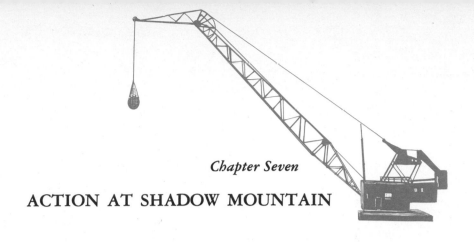

Chapter Seven

ACTION AT SHADOW MOUNTAIN

Tom's eyes were not used to the light. The two dark shadows were almost on top of him before he saw them!

Tom stopped and pulled back in the water. He saw that each of the men held a knife in his hand. Tom pulled his knife up and held it ready. Tom's teammate did the same thing. The frogmen knew they would have to fight their way out of the tunnel.

The submarine divers swam fast toward the two frogmen. Then the fight started! One of the submarine divers attacked Tom and tried to cut his air tube.

Tom grabbed the diver's hand. With all his strength Tom tried to make the diver drop the knife. But the diver pulled his hand away. Again he came at Tom with the knife. This time Tom grabbed the diver's arm. He pulled with all his strength. At last the knife dropped from the diver's hand.

Tom's teammate had taken the knife away from the

other submarine diver, too. The two submarine divers stopped fighting. They tried to swim back into the submarine base. But Tom and his teammate grabbed them. Each of the frogmen held his knife on one of the divers. Slowly they pulled them back out of the tunnel.

In a few minutes, the frogmen surfaced. Together they took the submarine divers to the shore. The other frogmen were waiting on the rocks for them. They tied up the two submarine divers.

The two men were very much afraid.

"Don't kill us!" one of them cried. "We will do anything you say."

"We will tell you everything," the other one cried.

"Good," said Tom. "We want to know about the secret sub base inside the mountain."

As the submarine divers told about the submarine base and the tunnels, the frogmen took down the information.

Then Tom asked the two divers if the submarine was inside the base right now.

"Yes," the first man told Tom. "We are just getting ready for our big attack on . . ."

The other submarine diver stopped him.

"Wait a minute," he said. "We don't have to tell these frogmen any more. In a few minutes our men will be out looking for us. They will rescue us. When the captain finds out that the Navy knows about the base, he will take the sub out of the base and go ahead with his plan right away."

"We will see about that," said Tom.

"You don't have enough men to stop the captain," said the other diver. "Before the Navy could get here to help you, the sub would be on its way with secret explosives to destroy the Navy base."

Tom did not answer the man. He walked away and called the other frogmen around him.

"We must move fast," Tom whispered. "That man may be right. If their captain finds out we are here, he may try to escape and attack the Navy base at once. We must stop him."

"What's your plan, Tom?" asked one of the frogmen.

"You are to go back to the *Sea Watch*," said Tom, pointing to two of the frogmen. "Radio the Navy base. Tell them we have found the secret sub base and that the submarine is inside. Tell them we will try to keep the sub inside the base until help comes. Take the two sub divers with you. Then come back to pick us up."

Then Tom turned to the team member who had first gone into the tunnel with him.

"You and I will put on the sub divers' rubber suits and swim into the secret base to look around. With the sub divers' suits on, no one will know who we are. We may be able to get all the information we need."

Tom then pointed to the last U.D.T. man.

"It will be up to you to keep the submarine inside the base," he said. "Take the explosives we have brought along and put them under the rocks at the base of the mountain. When my teammate and I have all the information we want on the base, we will swim out. I will give you the signal to set off the explosives. Enough rocks should drop down to cover the tunnel. That will give the Navy time to get here."

"What about Carlos?" asked Tom's teammate.

A look of worry came over Tom's face.

"I have been thinking about that," he said. "I will try to get information from the sub divers about Carlos. If there is any chance at all to rescue him, we will take it. I will take along one of our rubber suits for him to put on."

"What if the captain's men find you?" asked one of the frogmen.

"That's a chance we will have to take," said Tom. "If we are not back by a given time, the explosives must be set off to trap the sub."

For a minute the frogmen did not talk. Each man thought of how important his part of this mission was going to be.

Then Tom said, "Ready? We must move very fast."

Each man knew what he was to do.

When the submarine divers saw they were being

taken to the *Sea Watch*, they were afraid. They told Tom where Carlos might be found.

Tom and his teammate put on the submarine divers' suits. Then they swam out in the water. At Tom's signal the two men dived under the water. Soon they saw the opening of the tunnel. They swam into the dark tunnel, and before long they saw the water start to get light again. The two U.D.T. men knew they were inside the base. Slowly they swam up to the surface of the water.

The frogmen saw they were in a small harbor inside Shadow Mountain. The sea water came through the tunnel and made a harbor deep enough for a submarine to sail into. There were rocks all around the harbor. Great lights were placed on the rocks.

The submarine was docked at one side. Mines were being placed on its decks. A big crane picked up the heavy mines and set them down on the deck.

"It looks like they are getting ready to put out another mine field," thought Tom.

The two frogmen swam over to one side of the harbor and walked up on the rocks. No one said anything to them. As far as the men working inside the base knew, these were their submarine divers.

The two frogmen looked around the harbor. They would be able to give the Navy much information about this secret base.

Tom and his teammate walked around the harbor. They saw that many big chambers had been cut out of the rocks. Each chamber was full of guns and explosives. The submarine divers had told Tom that Carlos was kept in one of these chambers. Tom and his teammate looked in many of them.

All at once Tom stopped. He pulled his teammate down behind some rocks. Just ahead, Tom could see Carlos inside one of the chambers. Carlos was tied up. Two men stood talking to him.

Tom reached down for his knife. He knew that they would have only one chance to get to Carlos. If anything went wrong, they would never escape.

The two men had their backs turned to the U.D.T. men. One of them was talking.

"We have no more use for you," said the captain to Carlos. "This is your last day with us. My mate is waiting for me to tell him when to kill you."

The mate pulled out a gun and held it up.

"Before we kill you," said the captain, "I want you to know that we are ready to attack the Navy base. After that, war will start at once!"

"You won't get away with your plan," said Carlos.

"Won't we?" said the mate, pointing his gun at Carlos. "Who will stop us?"

Just then a call was heard.

"Captain! Captain!"

The captain and the mate turned and looked across the base. The call came from a man standing by the crane that was putting mines on the submarine.

"It must be that crane again," said the mate. "It has not been working right."

"We must get it working right away," said the captain. "The submarine must sail out of here very soon. I will go with you and see what the trouble is."

"What about Carlos?" said the mate.

"He can wait," said the captain. "That crane is more important than he is right now."

The two men walked down the rocks to the crane. Carlos was left alone in the chamber.

As soon as they saw the two men go, the U.D.T. frogmen ran to Carlos.

At first, Carlos did not know who the two divers were.

"We have come to get you, Carlos," whispered Tom, as he cut the ropes. "Put on this suit fast."

Tom handed Carlos the U.D.T. suit he had brought. Then Carlos knew who was talking to him.

"Tom!" he whispered. "How . . ."

Tom stopped him. "Fast, Carlos!" he said. "We don't have much time."

At once Carlos put on the rubber suit. Soon the two frogmen and Carlos were ready to try to escape.

"Our only way to escape," whispered Tom, "is to

swim out through the tunnel. We do not have another air tank for you, Carlos. Do you think you can make it that far holding your breath?"

"I think so," answered Carlos.

"Good," said Tom. "This chamber is not far over the water. When I give the signal, dive into the water and swim as fast as you can for the tunnel."

Tom looked out from the chamber to see if the way was clear. He pulled back as he saw the captain and the mate walking back down the rocks toward them.

"This is it!" said Tom. "It's now or never."

The captain and the mate had almost reached the chamber when Tom signaled.

The three men ran out from the chamber and dived off the rocks. The captain and the mate pulled out their guns and began firing at them.

"Stop them!" cried the captain. "They must be U.D.T. frogmen!"

More of the captain's men started firing down into the water.

The frogmen and Carlos swam down deep in the water. The shots did not reach them.

The captain ran down the rocks to the submarine.

"Get aboard the submarine," he cried to his men. "All is lost if the Navy traps us in here."

The captain ran up on the deck of the submarine.

"Get aboard!" he cried. "Faster! Faster!"

Chapter Eight

ESCAPE!

Outside the mountain, the two frogmen and Carlos reached the surface of the water. Carlos had just made it. He took several deep breaths of air when he came to the surface.

The men swam very fast for the rocks at the base of the mountain. The other U.D.T. frogman was waiting on the rocks for Tom's signal. He was ready to set off the explosives.

Inside the mountain, the captain's men ran to their places on the submarine. The big crane was just about to set the last mine down on the deck of the submarine. The captain looked up and saw the mine coming slowly down to the deck.

"Get that mine down here!" he called to the man working the crane. "Let the mine down faster. We must get away from this base at once!"

65

The man who was working the crane started to speed up the motor. The mine started to come down faster.

"Watch it!" cried the captain. "That mine is coming down too fast. It will go off if it hits the deck!"

The man in the crane tried to slow down the motor. But the crane was not working right. The motor would not slow down. The mine dropped faster and faster. Then it crashed into the deck!

A great explosion took place as the mine hit the deck of the submarine. One after another, the mines on the deck were set off. Great waves of water shot up from the explosions. Soon only small parts of the submarine floated on top of the water.

But the explosions did not stop with the submarine. The great explosion reached the chambers in the rocks where all the guns and explosives were. In no time at all, the explosives in the rocks around the harbor were set off, too.

Great rocks crashed down inside of the mountain! They dropped one after another into the small harbor. Soon the secret submarine base and all its men were gone.

Outside the mountain, the three U.D.T. frogmen and Carlos looked up and saw the rocks, snow, and ice on Shadow Mountain start to crash down into the sea.

"Into the water," cried Tom. "Swim for it, men. Fast!"

The three frogmen and Carlos dived into the water and swam away from the mountain. They swam away as fast as they could.

Great rocks and ice and snow crashed into the sea around the men! The rocks and ice made great waves as they crashed down into the water.

At last the men were clear of the crashing rocks. They headed for shore, away from the base of Shadow Mountain.

Once they were on shore, the men looked back. They saw the rocks and ice of Shadow Mountain still crashing into the sea.

"There is no need to worry about our explosives trapping the sub now," said Tom. "The secret tunnels are closed for good."

"What could have started all that?" asked Carlos.

"We will not know until the Navy gets here," said Tom. "But I don't think that sub will ever sail again!"

One more great rock crashed down into the sea. It sent a great wave of water up into the air. Soon the sea was still again.

The men saw one of the frogmen coming through the water in the rubber boat. He was coming to take them back to the *Sea Watch*.

Dan, Bill, and Andy were standing on the deck of the *Sea Watch* waiting for the rubber boat to come back. They had seen the rocks crashing off Shadow Mountain. They did not know what had taken place.

Just then they saw the rubber boat coming.

"There is Carlos!" cried Andy.

"They did it!" cried Dan. "The U.D.T. made it back and saved Carlos, too!"

Once the frogmen and Carlos were aboard, the crew of the *Sea Watch* grabbed Carlos by the hand.

"I never thought I would see any of you again," said Carlos, as he took their hands.

Then Tom and Carlos told the others all that had taken place.

"We had better get a message off to the Navy base," said Tom. "But how can we say all this, Dan?"

"It will be some message if we try to put down everything that has gone on," said Dan.

Andy heard the two men talking. He put a message down on a pad and showed it to Dan and Tom. When they saw what Andy had put down, the two men laughed.

"This does it, Andy," said Tom.

The crew of the *Sea Watch* and the frogmen stood around the radio and watched Tom send Andy's message:

SUB TRAPPED. CARLOS SAVED. MISSION OVER.

EXERCISES

Chapter One

THE STRANGE SUBMARINE

I. *Choose the right ending for each of these sentences.*

1. Dan and his crew were on their way
   a) to a Navy base in the north.
   b) to a war in a far country.
   c) to pick up some diving gear.

2. The *Sea Watch* and its crew were to
   a) look for a submarine.
   b) salvage ships.
   c) find a black boat.

3. Carlos called Dan to the deck to see a
   a) snow-covered mountain.
   b) Navy plane.
   c) strange submarine.

4. Dan had Carlos send a radio message
   a) to the Navy base.
   b) to the strange submarine.
   c) to the *Sea Watch*.

5. The submarine crew stopped firing at the *Sea Watch* when
   a) Carlos and Andy pulled the frogman aboard.
   b) the Navy plane came.
   c) Dan asked them to stop.

II. *Turn to pages 8 and 9 and see if you can find answers to these questions.*

1. When the men on the submarine saw the Navy plane, did they fire at it?
2. Did Dan tell Andy, Carlos, or Bill to radio the Navy base?
3. How much of the *Sea Watch* was destroyed by the submarine shell?
4. What did Carlos say that U.D.T. meant?

III. *Think about this sentence and then complete it in your own words.*

If I were the commander of the Navy base and found a strange submarine, I would:

Chapter Two

CARLOS TURNS FROGMAN

I. *Choose the right ending for each of these sentences.*

1. The frogman said his team had been sent on a mission to find
   a) the *Sea Watch.*
   b) a mine field.
   c) a submarine.

2. When Tom's team found the mine field, a strange submarine surfaced and
   a) sent men to help them.
   b) began to clear out the mines.
   c) began firing on the frogmen.

3. A message from the Navy asked the *Sea Watch* crew
   a) to get information about the mines.
   b) to get away fast.
   c) to come on to the Navy base.

4. On his first dive underwater, Carlos saw
   a) the strange submarine.
   b) a mine.
   c) more frogmen.

5. As Carlos was getting information about the mines,
   a) he was grabbed and held tightly.
   b) he lost one of his flippers.
   c) he was pulled slowly toward the surface.

74

II. *Turn to page 16 and see if you can find answers to these questions.*

1. Does the frogman suit fit loosely or tightly?
2. Does the suit cover the frogman's feet and hands?
3. Does the suit cover his head and face?
4. What was the frogman's suit made to do?

III. *Think about this sentence and then complete it in your own words.*

When Carlos could not be found, I think the men of the *Sea Watch* felt:

Chapter Three

THE U.D.T. FIGHTS BACK

I. *Choose the right ending for each of these sentences.*

1. When Carlos did not come up, Dan
   a) started to get ready to dive.
   b) told Tom to dive.
   c) told Bill to go to the Navy base.

2. Dan could not stay in the water long because
   a) of the mines.
   b) he could not swim very well.
   c) it was too cold.

3. When Dan could not find Carlos,
   a) Bill went down to look for him.
   b) Andy put out a life jacket for him.
   c) the *Sea Watch* started for the Navy base.

4. Commander Martin said that Carlos
   a) must have been a good man.
   b) must have put the mines in the sea.
   c) must have been a bad first mate.

5. Commander Martin took Dan to watch U.D.T. frogmen
   a) look for the submarine.
   b) destroy the mine field.
   c) look for Carlos.

II. *Turn to pages 23 and 24 and see if you can find answers to these questions.*

1. What time was it when the *Sea Watch* reached the harbor at the Navy base?
2. Who were waiting at the dock?
3. What was the U.D.T. commander's name?
4. Who saw the U.D.T. commander first, Dan or Tom?

III. *Think about this sentence and then complete it in your own words.*

I think the name *frogmen* is a good one because:

Chapter Four

CLEARING THE MINE FIELD

I. *Choose the right ending for each of these sentences.*

1. When the anchor was dropped, Commander Martin
    a) put on a heavy rubber suit.
    b) called the frogmen together.
    c) took off his gloves.

2. The U.D.T. commander showed where the mine field was
    a) on a map.
    b) at the base.
    c) in the water.

3. In each of the two rubber boats there were
    a) five frogmen.
    b) three frogmen and a commander.
    c) two frogmen and a map.

4. Each frogman of Team 485 took some explosives and
    a) went looking for the submarine.
    b) tied them to a buoy.
    c) tied them to a mine.

5. The work of clearing the mine field
    a) went on for two days.
    b) was done only by Team 485.
    c) went on all day.

II. *Turn to pages 27 and 28 and see if you can find answers to these questions.*

1. How many of the men who want to be frogmen complete the training?
2. Must a man be able to swim well before he can train to be a frogman?
3. Who are picked to be frogmen?

III. *Think about this sentence and then complete it in your own words.*

I think a frogman should be:

Chapter Five

THE SECRET SUBMARINE BASE

I. *Choose the right ending for each of these sentences.*

1. When Carlos came to, he was
   a) on the surface of the water.
   b) inside the strange submarine.
   c) in another country.

2. One of the two men standing over Carlos
   a) had on a frogman suit.
   b) had on glasses.
   c) held a gun in his hand.

3. The captain said he destroyed ships because
   a) he liked to see them go down.
   b) it was the mission of his country.
   c) he was going to start a war.

4. Carlos heard two men talking about a plan
   a) to destroy the Navy base.
   b) to set fire to the *Sea Watch*.
   c) to send the *Sea Watch* to the bottom.

5. The first mate of the submarine sent Carlos
   down to
   a) put explosives under the rocks.
   b) tie a message to the buoy rope.
   c) cut through the buoy rope.

II. *Turn to pages 39 and 42 and see if you can find answers to these questions.*

1. What did Carlos put into one of his heavy gloves?

2. What had been anchored over the tunnel?

3. What did Carlos do to the buoy rope while he was being pulled up slowly?

4. When he was almost to the surface, what did Carlos do with the plastic pad?

III. *Think about this sentence and then complete it in your own words.*

I think Carlos did right by going with the submarine captain and his men because:

Chapter Six

THE SEA WATCH'S MISSION

I. *Choose the right ending for each of these sentences.*

1. The *Sea Watch* was sent on a mission
   a) to destroy the strange submarine.
   b) to clear the mine field.
   c) to rescue Carlos.

2. The sonar on the *Sea Watch* picked up a small object. It was
   a) the submarine's demolition crew.
   b) the buoy with Carlos' message.
   c) a frogman in the water.

3. The message from the Navy base said:
   a) ANCHOR WHERE YOU ARE.
   b) TURN BACK TO NAVY BASE.
   c) ANCHOR IN COVE 962.

4. In teams of two the frogmen dived down and looked for
   a) a tunnel.
   b) fish for Andy.
   c) a plastic pad.

5. Inside the dark tunnel, Tom and his teammate did not see
   a) the submarine coming out.
   b) an octopus coming at them.
   c) two divers swimming toward them.

II. *Turn to page 46 and see if you can find answers to these questions.*

1. What did the sonar on the *Sea Watch* tell the man who listened to it?
2. How does the sonar work?
3. How did the sonar man know that the thing in the water was small?
4. Who was first to see what the sonar had picked up?

III. *Think about this sentence and then complete it in your own words.*

I think a sonar man's work would be:

Chapter Seven

ACTION AT SHADOW MOUNTAIN

I. *Choose the right ending for each of these sentences.*

1. After a hard fight, Tom and his teammate got
   the two submarine divers
   a) out of the tunnel and to the shore.
   b) back to the *Sea Watch*.
   c) tied up on the bottom.

2. Part of Tom's plan called for
   a) three frogmen to return to the boat.
   b) the submarine divers to go back in the tunnel.
   c) one frogman to set explosives in the rocks.

3. Tom and his teammate swam through the
   small tunnel and into
   a) a small harbor in Shadow Mountain.
   b) a large tunnel at the Navy base.
   c) the open sea.

4. Just as the captain and the mate were about to
   kill Carlos,
   a) Tom and his teammate hit them.
   b) a mine exploded.
   c) a man called the captain.

5. Tom and his teammate helped Carlos
   a) swim out of the tunnel.
   b) swim over to the submarine.
   c) tie up the captain and the mate.

II. *Turn to pages 57 and 58 and see if you can find answers to these questions.*

    1. What was done with the submarine divers?
    2. How many frogmen did Tom take with him into the secret base?
    3. What did Tom take with him for Carlos?
    4. How many U.D.T. divers were on the mission with Tom?

III. *Think about this sentence and then complete it in your own words.*

If I were going to swim into the secret base to look around, I would:

Chapter Eight

ESCAPE!

I. *Choose the right ending for each of these sentences.*

1. Inside the mountain, the captain's men ran to their places
   a) in the harbor.
   b) in the rocks.
   c) on the submarine.

2. Because the crane was not working right, a mine
   a) fell in the water by the submarine.
   b) crashed on the deck of the submarine.
   c) hit the captain and killed him.

3. The great explosion made rocks and ice crash
   a) only inside the tunnel.
   b) both inside the tunnel and out in the sea.
   c) on top of the *Sea Watch*.

4. The frogmen and Carlos got back to the *Sea Watch*
   a) by swimming.
   b) by going in a rubber boat.
   c) by Navy plane.

5. "SUB TRAPPED. CARLOS SAVED. MISSION OVER." This message was written by
   a) Dan.
   b) Tom.
   c) Andy.

II. *Turn to pages 65 and 66 and see if you can find answers to these questions.*

1. What made the big explosion take place?
2. Was the submarine blown up?
3. What happened to the explosives in the chambers in the rocks?
4. What happened to the submarine base and all its men?

III. *Think about this sentence and then complete it in your own words.*

If I were asked to be a member of a U.D.T. team, I would:

VOCABULARY

Frogmen in Action, the fifth book in the *Deep-Sea Adventure Series*, uses a vocabulary of 431 different words for a total of 11,685 running words. All but 142 words, which are italicized in the list below, may be considered basic vocabulary words. *Frogmen in Action* repeats 327 words from the first four books of the series, *The Sea Hunt, Treasure under the Sea, Submarine Rescue,* and *The Pearl Divers,* while adding 104 new ones.

a	been	*cover*	fast	had
able	before	*crane*	*faster*	hand
aboard	began	*crash*	*feel*	*harbor*
about	best	*crew*	few	has
above	better	cried	field	*hatch*
across	between	cut	fight	have
action	big		find	he
afraid	Bill	Dan	fire	head
after	black	*danger*	*firing*	heard
again	boat	dark	first	*heavy*
ahead	*bottom*	day	fish	held
air	*bow*	*deck*	*fit*	*helmet*
all	*breath*	*deep*	five	help
almost	brought	*demolition*	flew	here
alone	*buoy*	*destroy*	*flippers*	him
along	but	did	*float*	his
already	by	didn't	for	hit
always		*distance*	found	hold
am	call	dive	four	hope
among	came	*diver*	*frog*	how
an	can	*diving*	*frogman*	hungry
anchor	cannot	do	*frogmen*	hurt
and	*captain*	*dock*	from	
Andy	care	doesn't	full	
another	Carlos	don't		I
answer	*chamber*	down		ice
any	*chance*	*drop*		if
anything	*clear*		*gear*	I'll
are	close	each	get	I'm
arm	*closely*	*easy*	give	*important*
around	*closer*	enough	*given*	in
as	*code*	*escape*	glad	*information*
ask	cold	even	*glass*	*inside*
at	come	ever	gloves	into
attack	coming	everything	go	is
away	*command*	*explosion*	gone	it
	commander	*explosives*	good	it's
back	*cook*	eyes	got	
base	could		*grabbed*	
be	country	face	great	*jacket*
because	*cove*	far	gun	just

keep
kill
knew
knife
know

last
laughed
left
let
let's
life
light
like
listen
long
look
lost

made
make
man
many
map
Martin
mask
mate
may
me
mean
member
men
message
might
mine
minute
mission
more
morning
motor
mountain
move
much
must
my

name
Navy
near
need

never
next
no
north
not
now

of
off
on
once
one
only
open
or
other
our
out
outside
over

pad
parrot
part
pick
place
plan
plane
plastic
pointed
pull
put

radio
ran
reach
ready
real
rescue
right
rock
rope
rubber

said
sail
Salty
salvage
same
sat

save
saw
say
sea
secret
see
seen
send
sent
set
several
shadow
shape
shell
ship
shore
shot
should
shoulder
showed
side
signal
sir
skin
skipper
sleep
slow
slowly
small
snow
so
some
something
sonar
soon
sound
speed
stand
starboard
start
stay
stick
still
stood
stop
strange
strength
sub
submarine
such

suit
sunk
sure
surface
swam
swim

take
taken
talk
tank
team
teammate
tell
than
thank
that
that's
the
their
them
then
there
these
they
thing
think
this
those
thought
three
through
tied
tightly
time
to
together
told
Tom
too
took
top
topside
toward
train
trap
tried
trouble
try
tube

tunnel
turn
two

under
underwater
until
up
us
use

very

wait
walk
want
war
was
watch
water
wave
way
we
well
went
were
what
what's
wheel
when
where
which
while
whispered
who
why
will
wind
with
won't
work
worry
would

yes
yet
you
your